PUFFIN BOOKS

MATILDA'S HOW TO BE BRAVE

PUFFIN BOOKS

UK | USA | Canada | Ireland | Australia
India | New Zealand | South Africa

Puffin Books is part of the Penguin Random House group of companies
whose addresses can be found at global.penguinrandomhouse.com.

www.penguin.co.uk www.puffin.co.uk www.ladybird.co.uk

Penguin
Random House
UK

First published 2019

001

Written by Kay Woodward

Text design and incidental illustrations by Janene Spencer
Printed and bound in Great Britain by Clays Ltd, Elcograf S.p.A.

A CIP catalogue record for this book is available from the British Library

ISBN: 978–0–241–42815–3

All correspondence to:
Puffin Books, Penguin Random House Children's, 80 Strand, London WC2R 0RL

FSC www.fsc.org MIX Paper from responsible sources FSC® C018179

Penguin Random House is committed to a sustainable future for our business, our readers and our planet. This book is made from Forest Stewardship Council® certified paper.

MATILDA'S HOW TO BE BRAVE

ROALD DAHL

PUFFIN

CONTENTS

INTRODUCING MATILDA

This is Matilda.

You probably know this already. After all, this is a book about Matilda and there's a whacking great illustration of her on the cover. However, if you've never met her before, there is one thing that you should know about the star of this book before you learn anything else.

Matilda is *extraordinary*.

Here are some other words used to describe Matilda:

Astonishing

BRILLIANT

Sensitive

And most importantly:

BRAVE!

If you had to pick five fabulous words to describe yourself, what would they be?

1. ....

2. ....

3. ....

4. ....

5. ....

How to be BRAVE

Have you ever wanted to be brave, like Matilda?

Everything you ever wanted to know about Matilda is inside this book. (Unless you wanted to know something completely random, such as: can Matilda balance on one toe while juggling three watermelons? The answer is: probably. But we can't say for sure.)

Get ready to discover the countless qualities that make Matilda extraordinary. For starters, she's honest and fair and clever and funny and independent and wise. Yet she has one quality that shines particularly brightly: her bravery. Even when faced with one of the biggest bullies ever, Matilda stands up for what she knows is right. She doesn't let the bully win.

Perhaps you will open this book and say, 'Goodness! Matilda is so brave. How does she do it? Hey, if Matilda can be that brave, maybe I could be brave too?'

This is the perfect book to read if you're sitting in an armchair in a library, like Matilda. (Or anywhere else, actually.) It's also a remarkably good way to avoid the washing-up. Try it. If you're reading, grown-ups will let you get away with pretty much anything.

And that's not all. This is a book that's sprinkled with Matilda-tastic quizzes and puzzles and activities. You don't need to be a Matilda expert to do them.* Every clue you might need is already in this book. But **BE WARNED**. Once you've reached the last page, there's a rather big chance that you might want to read Roald Dahl's *Matilda* (if you haven't already read it, that is).

* Though you do need a pencil or pen.

WHO'S WHO?

Matilda isn't the only person in this book, of course. Here are some of the other characters you will meet.

Look at them carefully.

Matilda

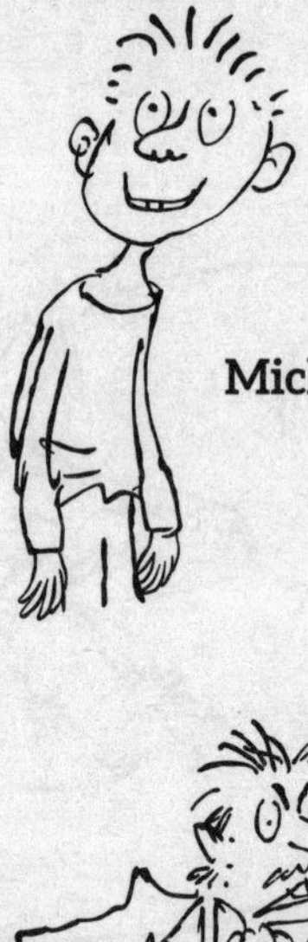

Michael

Miss Honey

Mr and Mrs Wormwood

Bruce Bogtrotter

Amanda Thripp

Miss Trunchbull

Did you look

REALLY HARD?

Good.

You may now

carry on.

FACT FILE:
MATILDA WORMWOOD

By the time she was one and a half: Matilda could speak perfectly.

By the time she was three: Matilda had taught herself to read.

By the time she was four years and three months old: Matilda had read all the children's books in the library.*

Likes: Books. Lots of books. Matilda is a great reader of books.

Dislikes: Eating off her knees while watching the telly, dishonest used-car salespeople and, above all, bullies.

Father: Mr Wormwood is a dishonest used-car salesperson who doesn't see anything wrong with tricking customers into paying for crummy second-hand cars that will break down very soon after they've bought them.

Mother: Mrs Wormwood is hooked on bingo and plays it five afternoons a week, leaving Matilda home alone. She likes eating off her knees while watching the telly.

Brother: Michael Wormwood is five years older than Matilda and goes to school. He is not extraordinary. He looks up to his father, who is training him to trick people into paying for crummy second-hand cars one day.

Good at: Being brave.

** Don't worry if you didn't finish reading all the children's books in the library by the time you were four years and three months old. This means that there are still a gazillion books for you to borrow, which is an exceptionally good thing.*

FACT FILE:

....

Now write a fact file that's all about YOU. Write your name in the space provided above.

Age: ....

By the time I was four years and three months old I could: ....

....

Likes: ....

....

Dislikes: ....

....

My most important people:

....

....

Draw yourself HERE.

Good at: ....

....

My favourite Roald Dahl book: ....

....

If I could be any Roald Dahl character, I would be:

....

If I could throw a custard pie at any Roald Dahl character, I would throw it at: ....

....

....

MATILDA'S Positively AWFUL PARENTS

You might think that Mr and Mrs Wormwood would be overjoyed to have an extraordinary daughter, but they are not. They don't really know what she's like. And they're not interested in finding out either.

> *Occasionally one comes across parents who . . . show no interest at all in their children, and these of course are far worse than the doting ones. Mr and Mrs Wormwood were two such parents. They had a son called Michael and a daughter called Matilda, and the parents looked upon Matilda in particular as nothing more than a scab. A scab is something you have to put up with until the time comes when you can pick it off and flick it away. Mr and Mrs Wormwood looked forward enormously to the time when they could pick their little daughter off and flick her away,*

preferably into the next county or even further than that.

It is bad enough when parents treat ordinary *children as though they were scabs and bunions, but it becomes somehow a lot worse when the child in question is* extra-ordinary, *and by that I mean sensitive and brilliant . . . Mr and Mrs Wormwood were both so gormless and so wrapped up in their own silly little lives that they failed to notice anything unusual about their daughter. To tell the truth, I doubt they would have noticed had she crawled into the house with a broken leg.*

QUICK QUIZ

After finding out all about Mr and Mrs Wormwood, do you think that they . . .

a) ☐ **might not be the best parents in the world?**

b) ☐ **don't deserve a daughter like Matilda?**

c) ☐ **should be picked off and flicked away like scabs themselves?**

If you answered **a), b) or c)** – or **all three** – CONGRATULATIONS. You are clearly neither half-witted nor gormless and are officially allowed to turn the page and carry on reading a book that is nearly as marvellous as Matilda herself.

The tricks of THE TRADE

Mr Wormwood is not just a used-car salesperson. He's also a great big fibber and a terrible cheat. Matilda doesn't approve of his behaviour one tiny bit. She quietly listens as her father explains how to make a gearbox appear to be running more smoothly by adding sawdust to the oil inside. Then he reveals his greatest trick of all: how to turn back the mileage. (Cars with lower mileage can be sold for much more money than worn-out old bangers.) His secret weapon is . . . AN ELECTRIC DRILL.

Matilda, who had been listening closely, said, 'But Daddy, that's even more dishonest than the sawdust. It's disgusting. You're cheating people who trust you.'

'If you don't like it then don't eat the food in this house,' the father said. 'It's bought with the profits.'

'It's dirty money,' Matilda said. 'I hate it.'

Two red spots appeared on the father's cheeks. 'Who the heck do you think you are,' he shouted, 'the Archbishop of Canterbury or something, preaching to me about honesty? You're just an ignorant little squirt who hasn't the foggiest idea what you're talking about!'

Matilda does NOT like dishonesty and she does NOT like tricksters who take advantage of other people.

Of the many mean things that Mr Wormwood does, which do you like the least, and why?

....

....

....

....

....

INTRODUCING the TRUNCHBULL

There are few people in the world as totally terrifying as the Headmistress of Crunchem Hall Primary School. Her real name is Miss Trunchbull, but she is more commonly known by her nickname of (drumroll, please – and make it a reeeeeeally long one) . . . THE TRUNCHBULL.

She was above all a most formidable female. She had once been a famous athlete, and even now the muscles were still clearly in evidence. You could see them in the bull-neck, in the big shoulders, in the thick arms, in the sinewy wrists and in the powerful legs. Looking at her, you got the feeling that this was someone who could bend iron bars and tear telephone directories in half. Her face, I'm afraid, was neither a thing of beauty nor a joy for ever. She had an obstinate chin, a cruel mouth and small arrogant eyes. And as for her clothes . . . they were, to say the least, extremely odd . . . She looked, in short, more like a rather eccentric and bloodthirsty follower of the stag-hounds than the headmistress of a nice school for children.

Of course, appearances can be deceptive. Take a box of chocolates, for example. The most delicious-looking chocolate could actually be quite yucksome inside. It might taste of something truly terrible like, say, carpet slippers or frogs. Or COCONUT. On the other hand, a chocolate might be shaped like something loathsome, like a Brussels sprout, but be filled with salty caramel. You just never know.

The same goes for people. Someone might LOOK foul and frightful but BE the sweetest, kindest person ever. Not in this case, though. The Trunchbull actually IS a tyrannical monster who likes nothing better than punishing her pupils.

Top advice to take away

1. Never ever, ever, ever annoy the Trunchbull. Ever.
2. Never eat a chocolate in case there's coconut inside.

THE TROUBLE with the TRUNCHBULL

The Trunchbull is unspeakably awful. She's rude, she's scary and she's cruel. But the very worst thing of all is that she's unfair. It's not just that the Trunchbull punishes pupils without listening to what they have to say. (That would be bad enough.) It's the fact that her punishments are BEYOND EXTREME too. Look what she does to poor Amanda Thripp, just because she is wearing pigtails.

> *Miss Trunchbull had now reached the victim and stood towering over her. 'I want those filthy pigtails off before you come back to school tomorrow!' she barked. 'Chop 'em off and throw 'em in the dustbin, you understand?'*

'My m-m-mummy thinks I look lovely, Miss T-T-Trunchbull,' Amanda stuttered, shaking like a blancmange.

'I don't give a tinker's toot what your mummy thinks!' the Trunchbull yelled, and with that she lunged forward and grabbed hold of Amanda's pigtails in her right fist and lifted the girl clear off the ground. Then she started swinging her round and round her head, faster and faster, and Amanda was screaming blue murder and the Trunchbull was yelling, 'I'll give you pigtails, you little rat!'

'Shades of the Olympics,' Hortensia murmured. 'She's getting up speed now just like she does with the hammer. Ten to one she's going to throw her.'

With a mighty grunt, the Trunchbull let go of the pigtails and Amanda went sailing like a rocket right over the wire fence of the playground and high up into the sky.

Using either complicated maths or pure guesswork, figure out where Amanda Thripp is going to land. Mark your answer with a cross.

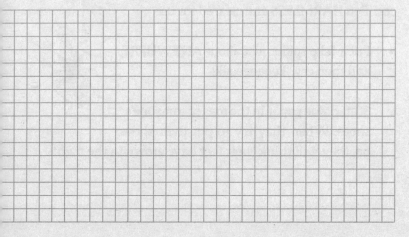

PRANKS

When someone treats her unfairly, Matilda doesn't stand for it. She gets her own back.

> *Most children in Matilda's place would have burst into floods of tears. She didn't do this. She sat there very still and white and thoughtful. She seemed to know that neither crying nor sulking ever got anyone anywhere. The only sensible thing to do when you are attacked is, as Napoleon once said, to counter-attack.*

If you've read *Matilda*, you'll already know that her pranks are a little on the DEFINITELY VERY DANGEROUS side. So the official advice is: REALLY DO NOT TRY THEM AT HOME. (Unless you want to be arrested, that is.)

But the good news is that not all pranks will land you in jail. The following gems have been certified HARMLESS and cleared for use.

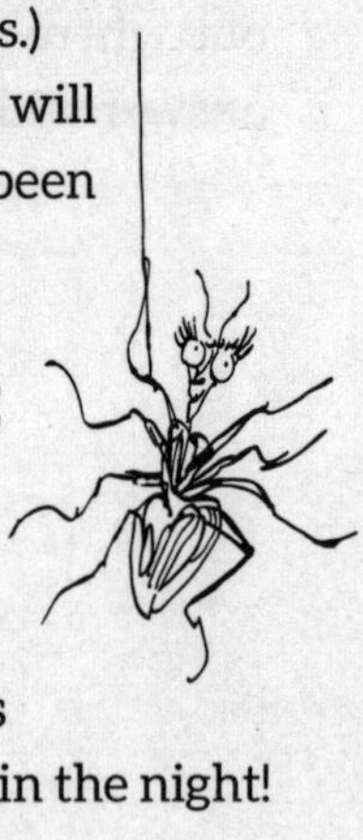

- Put a fake spider just about ANYWHERE and then cry, 'Eeeeeeeeek!'

- Stuff tissue paper in the toes of someone's shoes. When they try to put their shoes on, they will think their feet have grown in the night!

- Freeze half a glass of milk with a straw in it. Then top up the glass with fresh milk to give the illusion that it really is a perfectly normal drink. Now give it to someone and prepare to laugh yourself silly as they try to suck frozen milk through a straw.

Plan your own non-dangerous yet completely ingenious prank HERE.

ALL OVER THE WORLD

Did you know that Matilda loves to travel through space and time, discovering new worlds and meeting amazing people? 'How does she do this?' you might ask. 'Is there a time machine hidden under her bed? Is she so extra-extraordinary that she can FLY?'

Nope. It's better than that. (And a whole lot easier.)

It's not a time machine or an aeroplane that whisks Matilda all over the world. It's her imagination. That, and lots and lots of books. (Though, if Matilda were a real-life explorer, it's 100 per cent guaranteed that she'd be brave enough to go anywhere and meet anyone.)

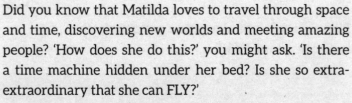

The books transported her into new worlds and introduced her to amazing people who lived exciting lives. She went on olden-day sailing ships with Joseph Conrad. She went to Africa with Ernest Hemingway and to India with Rudyard Kipling. She travelled all over the world while sitting in her little room in an English village.

Where would you like to go? It can be somewhere real or somewhere totally fantastical and completely made up. Your imagination can take you absolutely ANYWHERE.

If I could go anywhere at all, it would be:

When I get there I would:

INTRODUCING MISS HONEY

When she starts school, Matilda is put into a class with all the other youngest children. Their teacher is called Miss Honey and she charms her new pupils instantly.

> *Miss Jennifer Honey was a mild and quiet person who never raised her voice and was seldom seen to smile, but there is no doubt she possessed that rare gift for being adored by every small child under her care. She seemed to understand totally the bewilderment and fear that so often overwhelm young children who for the first time in their lives are herded into a classroom and told to obey orders. Some curious warmth that was almost tangible shone out of Miss Honey's face when she spoke to a confused and homesick newcomer to the class.*

Do you have a favourite teacher?

....

Can you think of three words to describe them?

1. ....

2. ....

3. ....

HONEY VERSUS TRUNCHBULL

In Roald Dahl's books, the names of his characters are sometimes Very Big Clues. They are a not-so-secret way of letting the reader know what a character is really like. Take Miss Honey and Miss Trunchbull, for example. Miss Honey sounds super sweet. And she is. Meanwhile, even if all you knew about Miss Trunchbull was her name, then you might already be able to guess that . . .

> *She was a gigantic holy terror, a fierce tyrannical monster who frightened the life out of the pupils and teachers alike. There was an aura of menace about her even at a distance, and when she came up close you could almost feel the dangerous heat radiating from her as from a red-hot rod of metal.*

But imagine if Miss Honey and Miss Trunchbull didn't have those names. What if you (yes, *you* – the clever-looking one holding this brilliant book) could give them brand-new names?

Guess what?

YOU CAN.

RIGHT NOW.

name: ....

name: ....

MATILDA'S LIMERICK

Matilda isn't just off-the-scale clever. She's also funny. And when she's asked to read out her limerick (a witty, rhyming poem) in Miss Honey's class, she goes ahead and reads it, even though she's nervous about being told off. So that makes her brave too.

Limericks are **five lines** long.

Limerick Rules

The **first line usually ends** with someone's **name** or a **place name**.

LINE **1** The thing we all ask about **JENNY**
LINE **2** Is, 'Surely there cannot be **MANY**
LINE **3** Young girls in the PLACE
LINE **4** With so lovely a FACE?'
LINE **5** The answer to that is, 'Not **ANY**!'

The **last words** of lines **1**, **2** and **5** must rhyme.

The **last words** of lines **3** and **4** must rhyme.

Here is space for you to write your own limerick. If you can make it rhyme, award yourself 10 points. If you can read it out to someone else and make them roll on the ground, clutching their sides and weeping hysterically with laughter, give yourself another 500 points.

I is for . . .

INTOLERABLE, INTIMIDATING and IRRITABLE. Unfortunately, there is no room to talk about those things here, because this is a book about Matilda, not the Trunchbull. However, I is also for **INDEPENDENT**, which is what Matilda most definitely is. If she can do something herself, she will.

'Where are the children's books please?' Matilda asked.

'They're over there on those lower shelves,' Mrs Phelps told her. 'Would you like me to help you find a nice one with lots of pictures in it?'

'No, thank you,' Matilda said. 'I'm sure I can manage.'

From then on, every afternoon, as soon as her mother had left for bingo, Matilda would toddle down to the library. The walk took only ten minutes and this allowed her two glorious hours sitting quietly by herself in a cosy corner devouring one book after another. When she had read every single children's book in the place, she started wandering round in search of something else.

I is also for **ICE CREAM**. Don't forget that.

Is there something you really want to do by yourself? Be inspired by Matilda and give it a go!

Books, BOOKS, BOOKS!

Matilda loves to read. After she's finished all the children's books in the library, she's brave enough to try books that grown-ups read, even those that have NO PICTURES AT ALL. The kindly librarian, Mrs Phelps, recommends a selection of classic novels, including *The Old Man and the Sea* by Ernest Hemingway (which quite a lot of grown-ups have always meant to read, but have never actually opened and are quite embarrassed that Matilda has read before them).

> *'Mr Hemingway says a lot of things I don't understand,' Matilda said to her. '. . . But I loved it all the same. The way he tells it I feel I am right there on the spot watching it all happen.'*
>
> *'A fine writer will always make you feel that,' Mrs Phelps said. 'And don't worry about the bits you can't understand. Sit back and allow the words to wash around you, like music.'*
>
> *'I will, I will.'*

List your top three books here. (They don't have to be written by Ernest Hemingway.)

1. ....

2. ....

3. ....

What would you like to write about? Here's space for your own brilliant ideas.

....

....

....

....

....

....

....

....

....

....

....

FUNNY BITS

Matilda shows that it's not just grown-ups who are wise. Children know a lot of clever stuff too. For example, Matilda has some important things to say on the subject of children's books.

'Who taught you to read, Matilda?' Miss Honey asked.

'I just sort of taught myself, Miss Honey.'

'And have you read any books all by yourself, any children's books, I mean?'

'I've read all the ones that are in the public library in the High Street, Miss Honey.'

'And did you like them?'

'I liked some of them very much indeed,' Matilda said, 'but I thought others were fairly dull.'

'Tell me one that you liked.'

'I liked The Lion, the Witch and the Wardrobe,*' Matilda said. 'I think Mr C. S. Lewis is a very good writer. But he has one failing. There are no funny bits in his books.'*

'You are right there,' Miss Honey said.

'There aren't many funny bits in Mr Tolkien either,' Matilda said.

'Do you think that all children's books ought to have funny bits in them?' Miss Honey asked.

'I do,' Matilda said. 'Children are not so serious as grown-ups and they love to laugh.'

What do you think? Is Matilda right? DO children love to laugh?

- ☐ Maybe.
- ☐ Absolutely, positively, definitely YES.
- ☐ What utter nonsense. I only like books that make me cry so hard that I look as if I've just chopped a hundred onions.

What ingredients do you think are vitally important in a children's book?

....

....

....

....

An ACTUAL FUNNY BIT

There will now be a short break, so that readers who love to laugh can enjoy a selection of Matilda-tastic jokes. Readers who do not love to laugh are instructed to close their eyes at once and turn to the next page before opening them again.

Did you hear the joke about the teacher who swallowed a clock?

It was time-consuming.

What do you call a terrifying headmistress with chocolate cake stuck in her ears?

Anything you like. She can't hear you.

What do snakes learn at school?

To read and writhe.

What do you call a boy with 9/10 written on his head?

MARK.

What do you call a girl standing between two goalposts?

ANNETTE.

What do you call a girl dressed from **HEAD TO TOE** in denim?

Jean.

Knock, knock.

Who's there?

Harry.

Harry who?

Harry up and let me in! I'm late for school!

What do you call a boy with a nose like a duck?

BILL.

What do you call a boy with a **SEAGULL** on his head?

Cliff.

The Very OPPOSITE of a SHOW-OFF

A show-off is a person who likes to tell everyone how fabulous they are at doing something. Mr Wormwood is a show-off. He likes to boast about how good he is at cheating other people. (**ALERT! ALERT!** Unless you want to turn out like Mr Wormwood, this is not a great idea.) And then there's Matilda, who is exactly the opposite. Someone so clever and brave could be excused for getting a teeny bit big-headed about it. However, even though Matilda has a lot of things she could show off about, she doesn't.

The nice thing about Matilda was that if you had met her casually and talked to her you would have thought she was a perfectly normal five-and-a-half-year-old child. She displayed almost no outward signs of her brilliance and she never showed off. 'This is a very sensible and quiet little girl,' you would have said to yourself. And unless for some reason you had started a discussion with her about literature or mathematics, you would never have known the extent of her brain-power.

Psst! What could you show off about if you really, really wanted to, but you don't because you're way too polite, like Matilda? Draw a picture of yourself performing your fabulous talent.

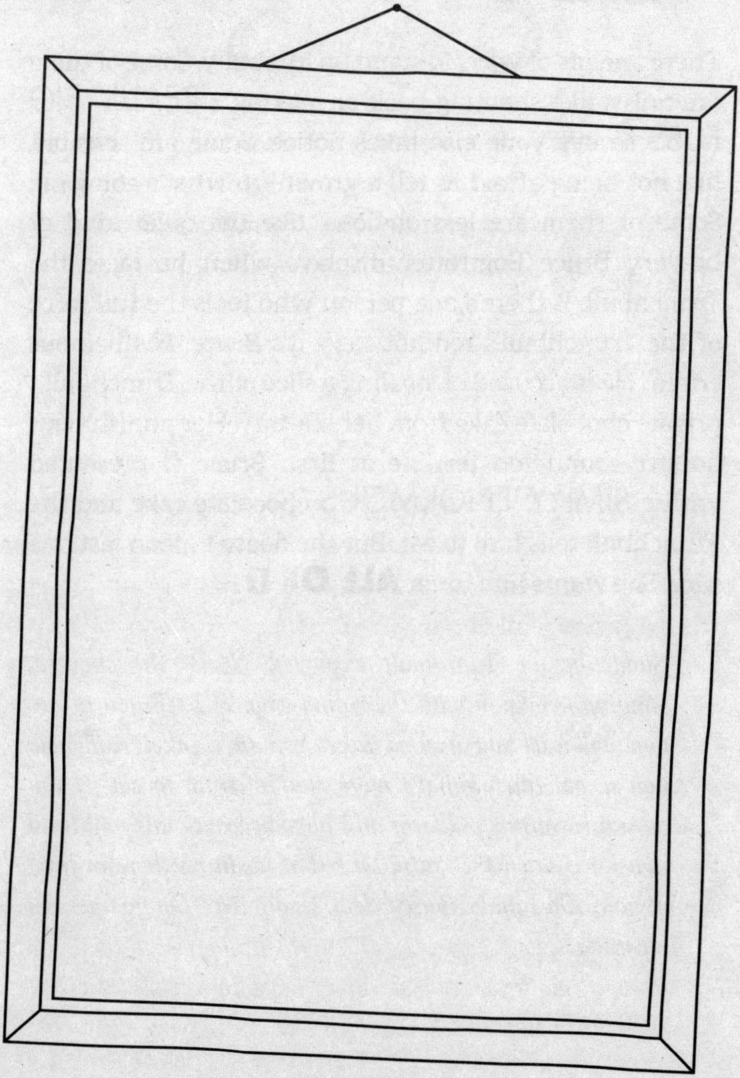

BRUCE BOGTROTTER

There are lots of ways to stand up to a bully. Some of them are noisy, like shouting back or making a REALLY BIG FUSS so everyone else takes notice. Some are sensible, like not being afraid to tell a grown-up what's going on. Some of them are less obvious, like the quiet kind of bravery Bruce Bogtrotter displays when he faces the Trunchbull. If there's one person who feels the full force of the Trunchbull's red-hot rage, it's Bruce. His heinous crime? He is accused of stealing a slice of the Trunchbull's private chocolate cake from her tea-tray. Her punishment doesn't sound too terrible at first. Bruce is presented with a SIMPLY ENORMOUS chocolate cake and the Trunchbull tells him to eat. But she doesn't mean just one slice. She wants him to eat **ALL OF IT**.

> *Suddenly the Trunchbull exploded. 'Eat!' she shouted, banging her thigh with the riding-crop. 'If I tell you to eat, you will eat! You wanted cake! You stole cake! And now you've got cake! What's more, you're going to eat it! You do not leave this platform and nobody leaves this hall until you have eaten the entire cake that is sitting there in front of you! Do I make myself clear, Bogtrotter? Do you get my meaning?'*

The boy looked at the Trunchbull. Then he looked down at the enormous cake.

'Eat! Eat! Eat!' the Trunchbull was yelling.

Very slowly the boy cut himself another slice and began to eat it.

So, did he do it? Did Bruce Bogtrotter eat the whole chocolate cake in one go?

If you've read *Matilda*, you'll already know the answer.

If you haven't read it, have a wild guess. You never know – you might be right!

Either way, turn this book upside down to find out.

Answer: Yes, Bruce absolutely did eat the whole cake. Go, Brucie!

BRUCE'S BRAVERY CAKE

Bake this gorgeously gooey and terrifically chocolatey cake for the brave people in your life. Taken from Roald Dahl's *Revolting Recipes*, this is the ACTUAL recipe for Bruce Bogtrotter's cake. We're not going to insist that you eat it all in one go, though. Not like the Trunchbull.

Make sure you ask a grown-up to help you with heating ingredients and with using the oven!

SERVES 1 TO 8

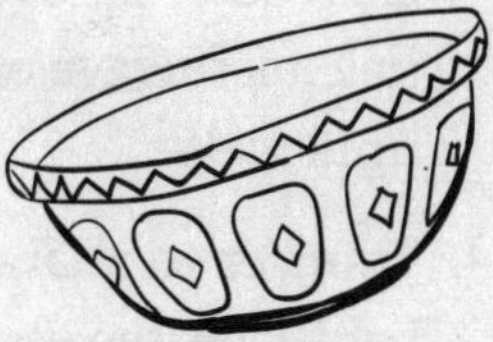

YOU WILL NEED

20cm (8 inches) round cake tin
baking paper
glass bowl
small saucepan
large mixing bowl
heavy-bottomed saucepan
wire rack
spatula

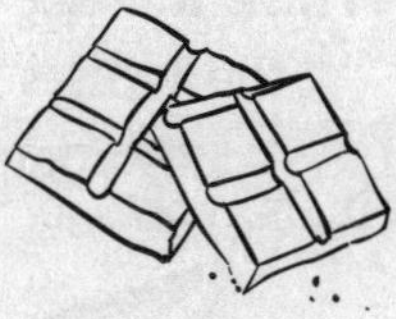

CAKE INGREDIENTS

225g (8 oz.) chocolate
170g (6 oz.) unsalted butter, softened
225g (8 oz.) plus 2 extra tablespoons caster sugar
35g (1 oz.) plain flour
6 eggs, separated, yolks lightly beaten

ICING INGREDIENTS

225g (8 oz.) chocolate
225g (8 fl. oz.) heavy cream

1. Preheat the oven to 180° Celsius (350° Fahrenheit).
2. Line the cake tin with baking paper, and butter the bottom and sides of the paper.

3. Ask a grown-up to help you melt the chocolate in a glass bowl set over a saucepan of simmering water or in a microwave on low heat. Mix in the butter and stir until melted.
4. Transfer to a large bowl and add the sugar, flour and lightly beaten egg yolks.
5. Whisk the egg whites until stiff. Gently fold half of the whites into the chocolate mixture, blending thoroughly, then fold in the remaining whites.

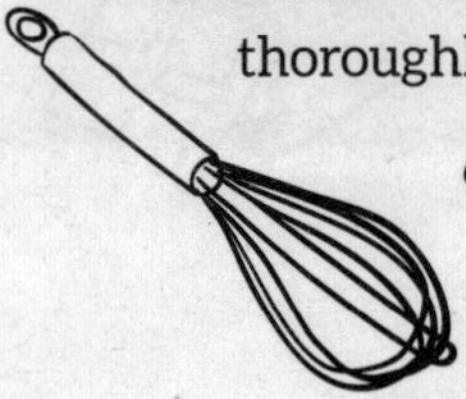

6. Pour the batter into the cake tin and bake for about 35 minutes. There will be a thin crust on top of the cake, and if tested with a toothpick the inside will appear undercooked (don't worry, the cake will get firmer as it cools). Remove from the oven, and cool in the tin on a wire rack.
7. While the cake is cooling, make the icing. Melt the chocolate with the cream in a heavy-bottomed saucepan over the lowest heat, stirring occasionally until the chocolate is fully melted and blended with the cream. Remove from the heat and cool slightly.

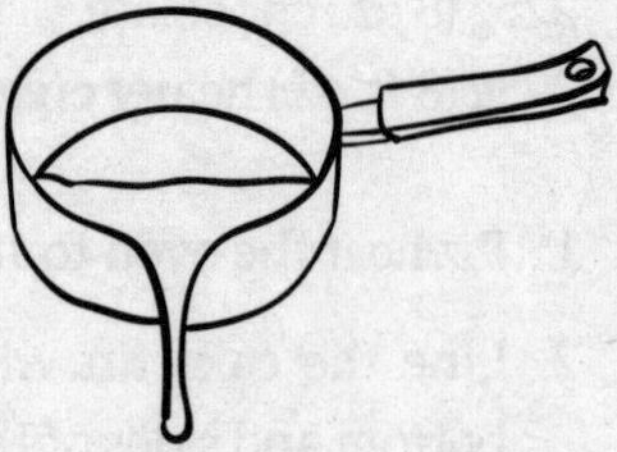

8. When the cake is cool enough to handle, remove it from the tin and discard the baking paper. The cake is prone to sinking slightly in the middle, so flip it upside down before icing it by placing a plate on top of the cake tin and carefully turning over the cake and plate together.

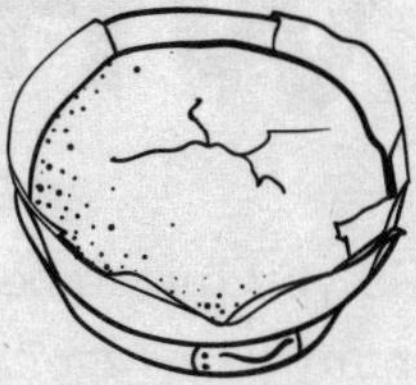

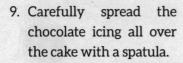

9. Carefully spread the chocolate icing all over the cake with a spatula.

So . . . WHO is WHO?

Do you remember meeting a bunch of characters many, many pages ago?

EXCELLENT.

In that case, you will be extraordinarily brilliant at matching these names with the mysterious silhouettes.

Choose from:

Amanda Thripp
Bruce Bogtrotter
Matilda
Michael
Miss Honey
Miss Trunchbull
Mr and Mrs Wormwood

....

....

....

Psst! Here's one to get you started: Matilda is top right on page 50! You're welcome.

GUTSY and ADVENTUROUS

Meet Lavender. She's another of Matilda's new classmates and they get along right away. Why? Because they share two wonderful qualities.

Among Matilda's new-found friends was the girl called Lavender. Right from the first day of term the two of them started wandering round together during the morning-break and in the lunch-hour. Lavender was exceptionally small for her age, a skinny little nymph with deep-brown eyes and with dark hair that was cut in a fringe across her forehead. Matilda liked her because she was gutsy and adventurous. She liked Matilda for exactly the same reasons.

What are the two qualities you admire most in your best friend and why?

1. ....

....

....

....

2. ....

....

....

....

To Catch a NEWT

At Crunchem Hall, the headmistress (that's the Trunchbull, in case you've spent the last fifty pages picking your nose) gives a weekly test in each classroom, striking terror into the hearts of pupils and teachers alike. As well as insisting that pupils are clean, speak only when spoken to, stand up to answer a question, never argue, never answer back and never try to be funny, the Trunchbull has one more rule. Whenever she enters a classroom, there must be a jug of water and a glass on the table. When Lavender hears this, she is suddenly inspired by the great heroines in her life: including, of course, Matilda.

Lavender decides to catch a newt and put it in the Trunchbull's water jug.

What would **YOU** put in the jug?

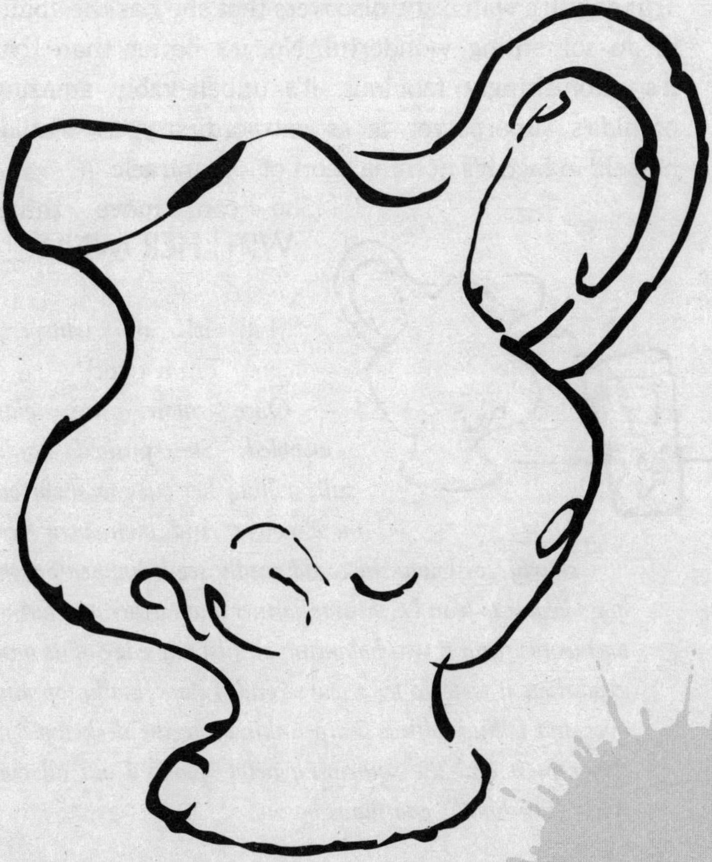

MATILDA'S SUPERPOWER

When Matilda gets the blame for booby-trapping the Trunchbull's water, she discovers that she has the ability to do something wonderful. No, it's better than that. It's astonishingly fabulous. It's unbelievably amazing. Matilda's superpower is as extraordinary as Matilda herself! In fact, it's nothing short of . . . a miracle.

She can move things WITH HER MIND.

'Tip it!' *she whispered again.* 'Tip it over!'

Once more the glass wobbled. She pushed harder still, willing her eyes to shoot out more power. And then, very very slowly, so slowly she could hardly see it happening, the glass began to lean backwards, farther and farther and farther backwards until it was balancing on just one edge of its base. And there it teetered for a few seconds before finally toppling over and falling with a sharp tinkle on to the desk-top. The water in it and the squirming newt splashed out all over Miss Trunchbull's enormous bosom.

If you had a superpower, what would it be? And what would you use it for?

Draw yourself using it right here.

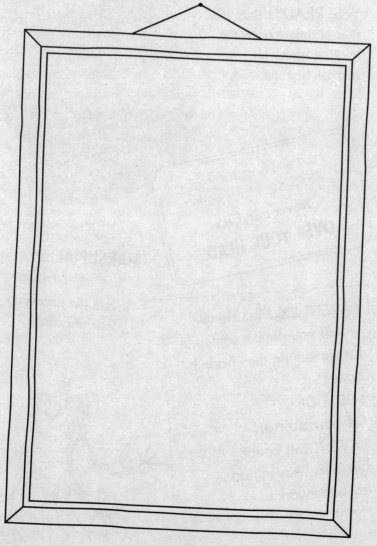

ANOTHER FUNNY BIT

YES, REALLY! Because there's always room for another funny bit. Just ask Matilda.

WARNING
Proceed at your own risk. If you split your sides laughing, the publisher cannot be held responsible. If, however, you have zero sense of humour, carry on. You should be absolutely FINE.

Did you hear the joke about the school roof?
Never mind, it's OVER YOUR HEAD.

Why was the **MARSUPIAL** hired to teach Year Three?
He had the necessary koalafications.

LAVENDER: Miss Honey, would you punish someone for something they hadn't done?
MISS HONEY: **Of course not!**
LAVENDER: Great, because I haven't done my homework.

Which fruit **NEVER PLAYS BY ITSELF** at break time?

A PEAR.

MISS TRUNCHBULL: You're late. You should have been here at nine o'clock.

LAVENDER: **Why? Did something happen?**

MISS TRUNCHBULL: You're *always* late.

LAVENDER: **Well, you keep ringing the bell before I get here.**

IT'S LIKE MUSIC

When Miss Honey recites a few lines from 'In Country Sleep', a poem by Dylan Thomas, to Matilda, she is awestruck.

> *There was a moment of silence, and Matilda, who had never before heard great romantic poetry spoken aloud, was profoundly moved. 'It's like music,' she whispered.*

Can you think of a poem that reminds you of music? If you can, then WOW! You're one step ahead of Matilda.

If, like Matilda, you've only just realized such poetry exists, then look in the poetry books in your school library to find a great poem there.

Either way, write it down in this handy poem-shaped space. And, if you feel brave enough, read it to a friend. Because great poetry is worth sharing.

Other PEOPLE'S FEELINGS

Some people thinking that being brave means being super blunt. They might say, 'Goodness, you look as if you got dressed in the dark.' Or maybe, 'That hairdo was last fashionable in 1972.' Although both of these comments might be true, neither is kind and neither will make the listener feel particularly tip-top.

Perhaps one of Matilda's greatest qualities is that she's wonderfully sensitive. This means that she is very aware of other people's feelings. She does all she can to avoid upsetting them. For example, when she figures out that Miss Honey doesn't have a great deal of money, she thinks carefully about how her teacher might feel before speaking. Because the last thing Matilda would want to do is upset Miss Honey or make her feel silly.

Miss Honey got a teapot from the cupboard and put some tea leaves into it. She also found half a small loaf of brown bread. She cut two thin slices and then, from a plastic container, she took some margarine and spread it on the bread.

Margarine, *Matilda thought. She really must be poor.*

Miss Honey found a tray and on it she put two mugs, the teapot, the half-bottle of milk and a plate with the two slices of bread. 'I'm afraid I don't have any sugar,' she said. 'I never use it.'

'That's all right,' Matilda said. In her wisdom she seemed to be aware of the delicacy of the situation and she was taking great care not to say anything to embarrass her companion.

To find out how sensitive you are, take this quick quiz.

If you meet your auntie or uncle at a party, would you tell them if . . .

1. They had a terrible hair do?
2. The colour they are wearing makes them look as if they're seasick?
3. They have a bogey sticking out of their nose?

Answers

1. Always tell someone they look marvellous, even if you don't think they do.
2. Always tell someone they look marvellous, even if you don't think they do.
3. Yes. Tell them NOW. They will thank you, truly.

WHO'S the BOSS?

Sometimes, being brave means letting someone else take charge. Traditionally, it's grown-ups who get to do all the bossing about. They're supposed to know way more than children. They've been around a bit longer, after all. (A LOT longer, in some cases.) But they aren't always right. Sometimes, children are the clever ones. Especially children like Matilda. When it's clear that Miss Honey is having a terrible time, but doesn't want to admit it, Matilda decides that it's time for a child to take charge and help a grown-up.

> *Miss Honey smiled. It was extraordinary, she told herself, how this little snippet of a girl seemed suddenly to be taking charge of her problems, and with such authority, too. 'Well,' she said, 'that depends on what the questions are.'*

Rank the people in your house in order of bossiness, from the least bossy to the one who is Bossy with a capital B. Make sure to include yourself!

Most bossy

↑

....

....

....

....

....

....

....

....

↓

Least bossy

The GREAT UNSCRAMBLING

Do you remember those characters you met at the very beginning of this book? You know, the ones that you correctly identified, just by looking at their silhouettes on pages 50 and 51? You do! Splendid. But can you attempt an even more fiendish puzzle? Can you unscramble the letters below to find the names of the characters who star in *Matilda*?

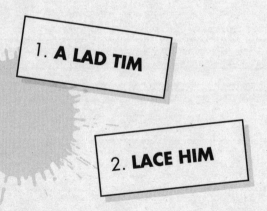

1. **A LAD TIM**

2. **LACE HIM**

3. **MR AND MRS WOODWORM**

4. **SHINY SOME**

5. **BOT BUTTER GROCER**

6. **ARMPIT DAPHNA**

7. **BLUNT CRUSH SLIM**

1. MATILDA 2. MICHAEL 3. MR AND MRS WORMWOOD
4. MISS HONEY 5. BRUCE BOGTROTTER 6. AMANDA THRIPP
7. MISS TRUNCHBULL

HEROES and VILLAINS

Matilda is a hero, which is a terrific thing to be. (If you have any spare time, you could give it a go. You don't have to rescue a cat from the top of the Empire State Building, though. Sometimes, offering to clean the fish tank is enough to convince a parent that you're a hero. Seriously.) There are many reasons why Matilda is a hero. Here are a few: she's brave; she helps others; and she stands up for herself, even when faced with the biggest bully in the world. Here, the Trunchbull is bullying Miss Honey . . . until Matilda steps in.

> *'. . . Read Nicholas Nickleby, Miss Honey, by Mr Dickens. Read about Mr Wackford Squeers, the admirable headmaster of Dotheboys Hall. He knew how to handle the little brutes, didn't he! He knew how to use the birch, didn't he! He kept their backsides so warm you could have fried eggs and bacon on them! A fine book, that. But I don't suppose this bunch of morons we've got here will ever read it because by the look of them they are never going to learn to read anything!'*
>
> *'I've read it,' Matilda said quietly.*

Can you match these heroes and villains with their descriptions . . .?

Miss Honey

Miss Trunchbull

Mr Wormwood

Bruce Bogtrotter

Lavender

FIERCE, TYRANNICAL MONSTER

MILD, KIND SOUL

BRAVE, RESOURCEFUL RASCAL

ARROGANT, PATRONIZING CHEAT

BELCHING, WORLD-BEATING TROOPER

YET ANOTHER FUNNY BIT

Which Roman emperor suffered from **HAYFEVER?**

Julius Sneezer.

Which **FRUIT** launched a thousand ships?

Melon of Troy.

Who was the biggest **ROBBER** in history?

Atlas. He held up the whole world.

Who refereed a **TENNIS** match between Caligula and Nero?

A Roman Umpire.

Where would you find **HADRIAN'S WALL?**

At the bottom of Hadrian's garden.

How do you use an ancient Egyptian **DOORBELL?**

Toot and come in.

Which **PHARAOH** played the trumpet?

Tooting-khamun.

How can you tell when a **MUMMY** is angry?

He flips his lid.

How to BEAT a BULLY

The Trunchbull is a bully. Full stop. She terrorizes all who meet her . . . except one person. And that's Matilda. So what's Matilda's secret? How does she stand up to one of the most vile villains of all time? Calmly, quietly and with dignity. Bravo! And then she comes up with a plan so clever – and so miraculous – that the Trunchbull is history. We're not going to tell you how Matilda does it, though. Sorry about that. You'll have read *Matilda* to find out. But, for those who have already read the book, ISN'T IT THE MOST BRILLIANT PLAN EVER?! Didn't you just love the bit where – oooh, wait! Don't spoil it for those who haven't read it yet.

SHHHH!

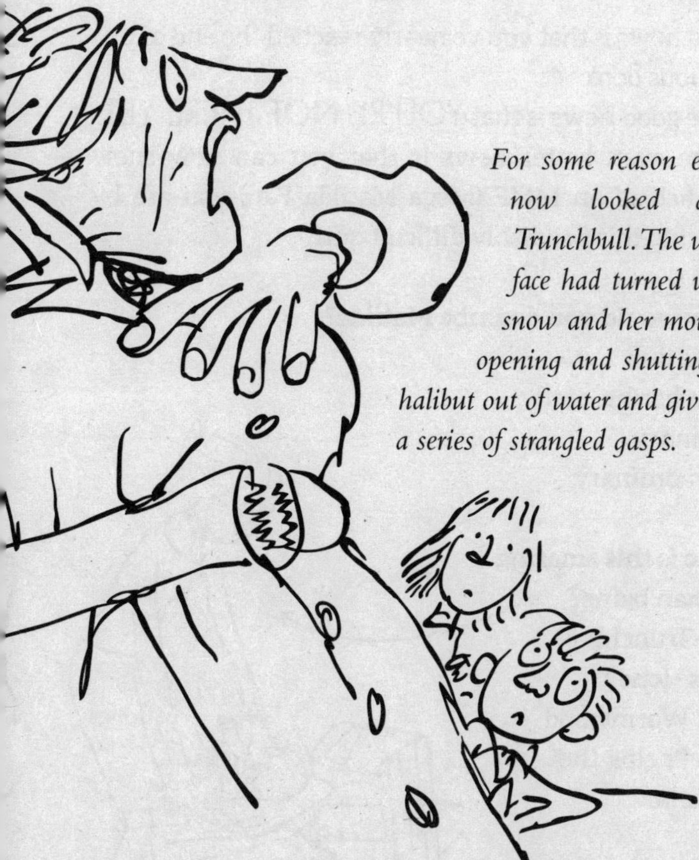

For some reason everyone now looked at the Trunchbull. The woman's face had turned white as snow and her mouth was opening and shutting like a halibut out of water and giving out a series of strangled gasps.

The MEGA *MATILDA* QUIZ

The bad news is that you've nearly reached the end of this marvellous book.

The good news is that YOU'RE NOT THERE YET. And the even better news is that you can now show how much of an MMF (Mega Matilda Fan) you are by completing this fiendishly difficult quiz.*

1. How would you describe Matilda?

a) Quite dull
b) A bit boring, really
c) Ordinary
d) Extraordinary

2. Who is this amazing human being?

a) The Trunchbull
b) Miss Honey
c) Mrs Wormwood
d) Mrs Phelps, the librarian

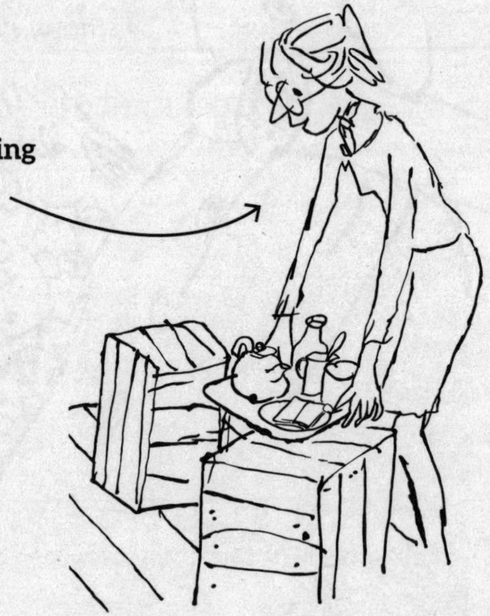

3. **Complete this sentence: By the time she was four years and three months old, Matilda had . . .**
a) swum the English Channel.
b) climbed Mount Kilimanjaro.
c) read all the children's books in the library.
d) learned to drive.

4. **What is Mr Wormwood's job?**
a) He is a used-car salesperson.
b) He is a tax inspector.
c) He is a parkour champion.
d) He is a teacher.

5. **What is the name of the school Matilda attends?**
a) Munchem Hall Primary School
b) Chewem Hall Primary School
c) Swallowemwhole Hall Primary School
d) Crunchem Hall Primary School

6. **What doesn't the Trunchbull like about Amanda Thripp?**
a) Her sunny personality
b) Her pigtails
c) Her charming button nose
d) Her incredible ability to spin on her head

* Don't worry – it's not that fiendish. Remember, all the answers can be found somewhere in this book. (And the actual answers are on pages 84 – 85.)

The MEGA MATILDA QUIZ Goes On

7. **What does Matilda use to discover new worlds?**
a) A very fast car
b) A hot-air balloon
c) Her imagination
d) The internet

8. **What is the name of Matilda's teacher?**
a) Miss Sugar
b) Miss Molasses
c) Miss Syrup
d) Miss Honey

9. **What is a limerick?**
a) A low, stone wall
b) A witty, rhyming poem
c) A type of banjo
d) A remedy for indigestion

10. Which of these words beginning with I describes Matilda?

a) Independent
b) Intolerable
c) Intimidating
d) Irritable

11. Matilda has read one of these grown-up books. But which one?

a) *The Invisible Man* by Ralph Ellison
b) *Frankenstein* by Mary Shelley
c) *The Old Man and the Sea* by Ernest Hemingway
d) *The Third Man* by Graham Greene

12. What does Matilda think that all children's books should have in them?

a) Illustrations
b) A challenging plot
c) Sad bits
d) Funny bits

The VERY LAST Bit of the MEGA MATILDA QUIZ

13. What type of cake does Bruce Bogtrotter eat?

a) Coffee and walnut
b) Victoria sponge
c) Lemon drizzle
d) Chocolate

14. Complete this sentence: Matilda admires people who are . . .

a) gutsy and adventurous.
b) plucky and brave.
c) inventive and hilarious.
d) kind and fair.

15. What does Lavender put into the Trunchbull's water jug?

a) A newt
b) A toad
c) A prawn
d) An octopus

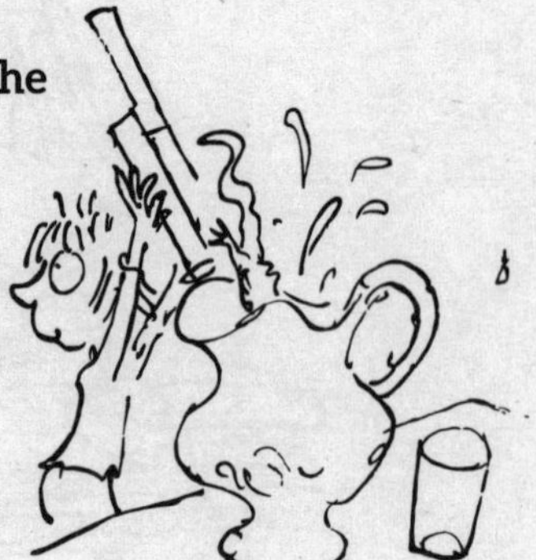

16. Miss Honey makes Matilda a snack of bread and what?

a) Butter
b) Margarine
c) Chocolate spread
d) Pickled herrings

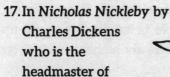

17. In *Nicholas Nickleby* by Charles Dickens who is the headmaster of Dotheboys Hall?

a) Walter Squirts
b) Wally Squabble
c) Wesley Squanders
d) Wackford Squeers

18. What is Matilda most famous for being?

a) Brooding
b) Bombastic
c) Boastful
d) Brave

MATILDA'S MIX-UP

It's time to test your phenomenal powers of observation! Can you find all of the people below in this mixed-up word-search grid? Matilda is already highlighted for you to get you going!

Amanda Thripp

Bruce Bogtrotter

Lavender

Michael

Mr Wormwood

Miss Honey

Matilda

Hortensia

Miss Trunchbull

Mrs Phelps

T	M	C	R	M	I	M	G	W	L	E	P	R	N	W
C	J	T	E	I	B	I	H	V	M	T	P	E	U	U
I	E	S	T	S	N	C	V	V	N	M	I	D	G	P
Y	F	H	T	S	K	H	S	J	Z	I	R	N	Z	H
S	X	L	O	T	M	A	Q	Y	L	S	H	E	P	H
E	D	K	R	R	K	E	M	R	W	S	T	V	D	C
T	A	N	T	U	T	L	T	V	B	H	A	A	Y	X
A	U	F	G	N	G	E	U	E	H	O	D	L	O	N
J	X	O	O	C	N	T	N	X	G	N	N	F	I	J
O	P	K	B	H	J	X	Z	S	N	E	A	M	G	W
M	L	M	E	B	D	S	R	X	I	Y	M	Q	E	S
X	T	Y	C	U	H	Y	L	L	A	A	A	B	L	Z
G	B	O	U	L	M	R	W	O	R	M	W	O	O	D
G	A	Q	R	L	S	P	L	E	H	P	S	R	M	P
D	M	B	B	M	A	T	I	L	D	A	F	C	M	O

See page 86 for the answers.

TEN TIMES AS BRAVE

Matilda is, of course, both **BRAVE** and **HEROIC**. But she is also very clever and knows lots of words that mean the same thing, having read the thesaurus in the library. (A thesaurus is a book with words that mean the same things as other words, not some kind of dinosaur, of course.)

There are many words to describe why Matilda is brilliant. Here are **ten**!

- **COURAGEOUS**
- **BOLD**
- **DAUNTLESS**
- **VALIANT**
- **INTREPID**
- **GALLANT**
- **FEARLESS**
- **AUDACIOUS**
- **BRAVE**
- **HEROIC**

Can you fit these ten words into the grid below? There are two answers filled in already to get you started.

PS Use a pencil because this is tricky!

See page 87 for the answers.

ANSWERS

Strictly no peeking until you've completed the MEGA MATILDA QUIZ!

1. d)

2. b)

3. c) Although if she'd had the opportunity, there's no doubt Matilda could have done all the other things too.

4. a)

5. d)

6. b)

7. c)

8. d)

9. b)

10. a)

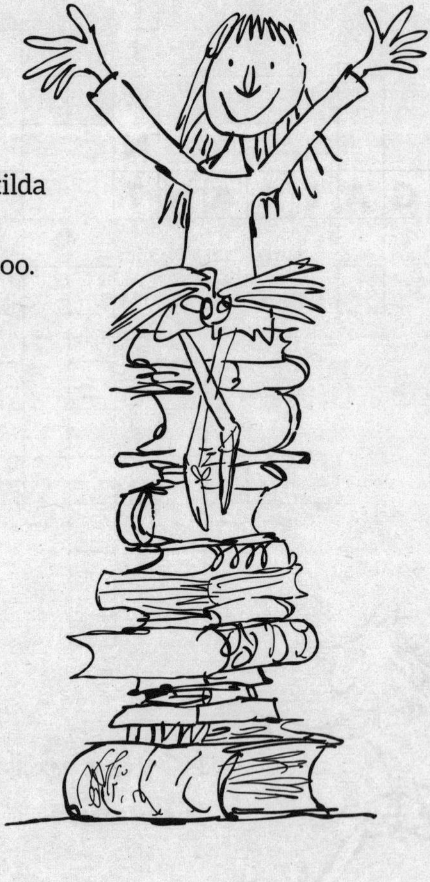

11. c) Though there's every chance she has read the others too.

12. Definitely d)

13. d)

14. Matilda admires her friend Lavender, who is gutsy and adventurous, so the answer is a). But, as Matilda is sure to admire people with all of these qualities, give yourself a point for *any* answer.

15. a)

16. b)

17. d)

Congratulations if you got this one right! The answer was easy to miss!

18. d) Of course.

MORE ANSWERS

MATILDA'S MIX-UP

T	M	C	R	M	I	M	G	W	L	E	P	R	N	W
C	J	T	E	I	B	I	H	V	M	T	P	E	U	U
I	E	S	T	S	N	C	V	V	N	M	I	D	G	P
Y	F	H	T	S	K	H	S	J	Z	I	R	N	Z	H
S	X	L	O	T	M	A	Q	Y	L	S	H	E	P	H
E	D	K	R	R	K	E	M	R	W	S	T	V	D	C
T	A	N	T	U	T	L	T	V	B	H	A	A	Y	X
A	U	F	G	N	G	E	U	E	H	O	D	L	O	N
J	X	O	O	C	N	T	N	X	G	N	N	F	I	J
O	P	K	B	H	J	X	Z	S	N	E	A	M	G	W
M	L	M	E	B	D	S	R	X	I	Y	M	Q	E	S
X	T	Y	C	U	H	Y	L	L	A	A	A	B	L	Z
G	B	O	U	L	M	R	W	O	R	M	W	O	O	D
G	A	Q	R	L	S	P	L	E	H	P	S	R	M	P
D	M	B	B	M	A	T	I	L	D	A	F	C	M	O

TEN TIMES AS BRAVE

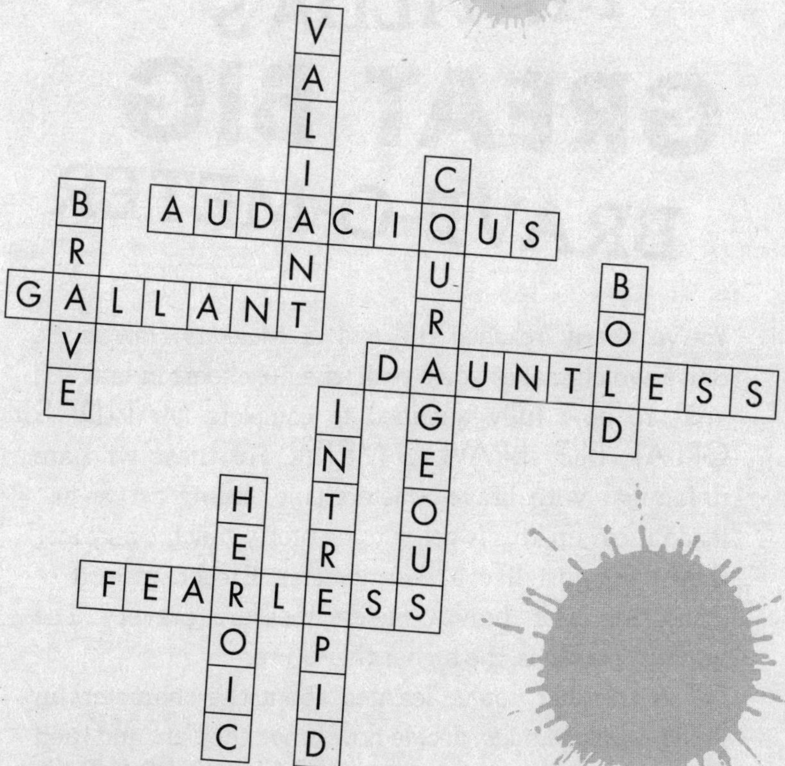

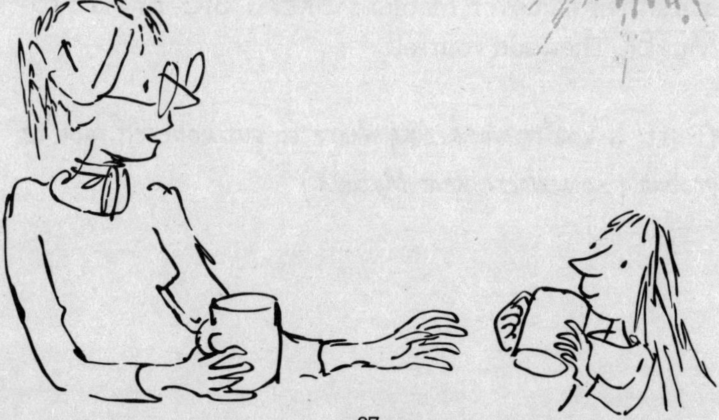

MATILDA'S GREAT BIG BRAVE-O-METER

You've nearly reached the end of *Matilda's How to Be Brave*, which makes you a real, true-life expert in bravery. You are now fully qualified to complete MATILDA'S GREAT BIG BRAVE-O-METER. For those who are unfamiliar with brave-o-meters (and, seeing as we just made them up, this is going to be pretty much everyone), they work just like a thermometer. Except, instead of measuring heat, brave-o-meters measure bravery. The braver a person is, the higher they score.

With what you've learned about the characters in Roald Dahl's *Matilda*, decide how brave they are and then mark their names on Matilda's GREAT BIG BRAVE-O-METER. Then add yourself.

(Psst! If you're wondering where to put yourself, you're probably somewhere near Matilda.)

SUPERBRAVE

....

....

....

BRAVE

....

....

....

QUITE BRAVE

....

....

....

SOMETIMES BRAVE

....

....

....

NOT VERY BRAVE

....

....

....

MEEK

....

QUENTIN BLAKE has illustrated more than three hundred books and was Roald Dahl's favourite illustrator.

In 1980 he won the prestigious Kate Greenaway Medal. In 1999 he became the first ever Children's Laureate and in 2013 he was knighted for services to illustration.

ROALD DAHL was a spy, ace fighter pilot, chocolate historian and medical inventor.

He was also the author of *Charlie and the Chocolate Factory*, *Matilda*, *The BFG* and many more brilliant stories. He remains

THE WORLD'S NUMBER ONE STORYTELLER.

HOW MANY HAVE YOU READ?

FEWER THAN 5?

WHOOPSY-SPLUNKERS!

You've got some reading to do!

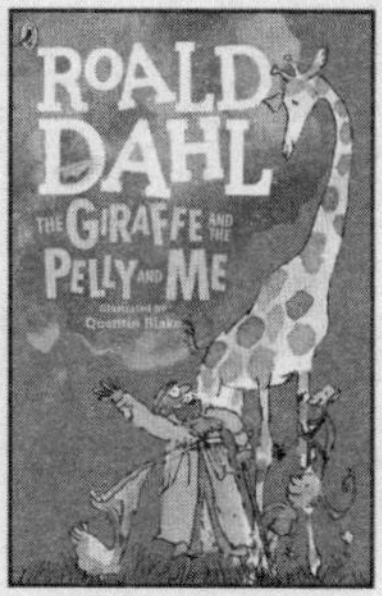

BETWEEN 5 AND 10?

Wonderful surprises await!

Keep reading . . .

MORE THAN 10?

Whoopee!

Which was your favourite?

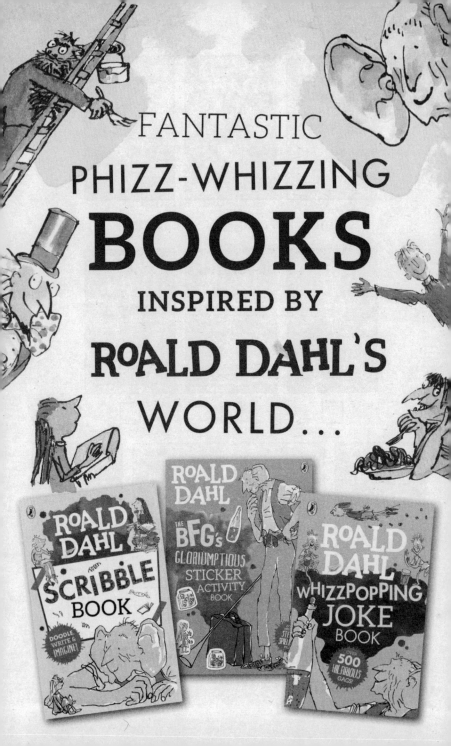

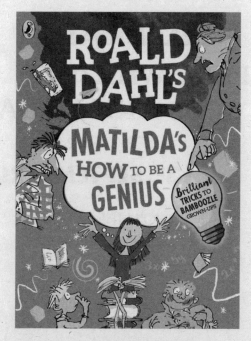